NATURAL HISTORIES

Histoires

Naturelles

Jules Renard

Natural Histories

TRANSLATED FROM THE FRENCH

BY ELIZABETH ROGET

ILLUSTRATIONS BY *Toulouse-Lautrec*

GEORGE BRAZILLER · NEW YORK

Contents

6

7

NATURAL HISTORIES

The Picture Hunter

HE jumps up early from his bed and sets out only if his mind is clear, his heart pure, his body light as a summer garment. He carries no provisions. Along the road, he will drink fresh air and inhale wholesome smells. He leaves his firearms at home, content with keeping his eyes open. His eyes serve as nets in which pictures are caught.

The first one he snares is that of the road, showing its bones of polished stones and the broken veins of its ruts, between hedges laden with blackberries and small wild plums.

Then he catches the picture of the river. Whitening at the elbows, it sleeps under the gentle stroke of willows. It glistens when a fish turns up its belly, as though a piece of silver has been thrown in; if a light rain falls, the river has goose flesh.

He picks up the picture of the moving wheat, the toothsome clover, the meadows hemmed in with rivulets. He seizes in passing the flight of a lark or a goldfinch.

Then he enters the woods. He did not know that his senses could take in so much. He is soon impregnated with scents, he misses not a single muffled sound, and his nerves attach themselves to the veins of leaves so that he may communicate with the trees.

Before long, he is vibrating to the point of discomfort, he is perceiving too much, he is in ferment, he is afraid, he leaves the woods and follows from a distance the peasants returning to the village.

Outside, he stares for a moment, with eyes ready to burst, at the setting sun as, on the horizon, it divests itself of its luminous garments, its scattered clouds.

Home at last, his head full, he puts out his lamp and, before going to sleep, delights in counting up his pictures.

Obediently, they appear again as his memory calls them. Each one wakens another, and new ones constantly join the phosphorescent band, like partridges that, all day pursued and divided, come together in the evening and, safe in the depth of furrows, sing and remember.

11

Coqs

Cocks

HE has never crowed. He has never spent a night in a hen house or known a single hen.

He is made of wood, with an iron leg growing out of his belly, and for years and years he has lived on top of an old church, the like of which no one dares build nowadays. It looks like a barn, and the ridge of its roof is as straight as the back of an ox.

But now masons appear at the other end of the church.

The wooden cock looks at them, and then suddenly a gust of wind forces him to turn his back.

And every time he looks again, new stones have blocked off a bit more of the horizon.

Before long, lifting his head with a jerk, he catches sight, at the top of the steeple that has just been finished, of a young cock that was not there this morning. This stranger carries his tail high, opens his beak like a singer, and, shiny new, wing on hip, he sparkles in the sunlight.

At first, the two cocks engage in a competition of mobility. But the old one is soon tired, and gives up. Under his single foot, the roof beam threatens to collapse. He leans over stiffly, ready to fall. He grinds to a stop.

And here come the carpenters.

They knock down this worm-eaten corner of the

13

church, take down the cock, and carry him about the village. For a fee, you may touch him.

Some give an egg, others a sou, and Mme. Loriot gives a silver piece.

The carpenters buy themselves drinks, and, after having quarreled over which one should own the cock, they decide to burn him.

Having built a nest for him out of straw and kindling, they set fire to it.

The wooden cock crackles brightly, and his flame rises up to heaven, which he has well won.

2

Every morning, after jumping off his roost, the cock looks to see if the other is still there—and the other always is.

The cock can boast of having beaten every rival on earth—but the other one is the invincible rival, the one out of reach.

The cock crows again and again; he calls, he provokes, he threatens—but the other answers only at certain hours, and at first does not answer at all.

The cock preens himself, puffing out his feathers—which are not bad at all, some blue and some silver—but the other one, up there in the blue sky, is a dazzling gold.

The cock calls his hens together, and marches

at their head. See—they belong to him, all love him and fear him—but the one up there is the adored of swallows.

The cock expends all of himself: he leaves here and there his marks of love, and, with sharp cries, achieves small triumphs—but the one up there is celebrating his nuptials, and his wedding bells peal out over the village.

The cock sharpens his spurs for a combat to the death; his tail looks like a cape draped over a rapier. His comb bursting with blood, he defies every cock in the sky—but the other one, who faces fearlessly into the storm, happens to be playing with the breeze, and turns his back.

And so the cock exacerbates himself until the end of day.

His hens, one by one, go home. He is left alone, hoarse, worn out, in the darkening yard—while the other one, resplendent in the last rays of the sun, sings with his clear voice the peaceful Angelus of evening.

Canards

Ducks

IT's the female that goes first, limping with both feet, to muddle around the hole she knows.

The drake comes after. The points of his wings are folded over his back and he, too, limps with both feet.

The duck and the drake walk in silence, as though they were going to a business meeting.

The duck lets herself slide into the muddy water in which float feathers, droppings, a vine leaf, straw. She almost disappears.

She is waiting. She is ready.

The drake goes in next, drowning his rich colors. All you see of him is his green head and the curl of his tail. They are comfortable in there. The water is warm. It is never emptied, and renews itself only in a rainstorm.

With his flattened beak, the drake nibbles and holds the back of the duck's neck. For a moment, he is in movement: the water is so thick that it hardly gives a ripple. Quickly calmed, smooth again, it reflects, on a black background, a corner of blue sky.

The duck and the drake no longer move. The sun warms them and puts them to sleep. You could pass by without noticing them. They are betrayed only by a few bubbles that burst slowly on the surface of the putrid water.

The Hen

FEET together, she jumps out of the chicken coop as soon as the door is opened.

She is a common hen, modestly attired, and she never lays golden eggs.

Blinded by the light, she takes a few uncertain steps in the barnyard.

What first meets her eye is the heap of ashes in which she takes her daily bath.

She rolls in it, plunges into it, and, with a great fluttering of wings and blowing up of feathers, she shakes off the night's fleas.

Then she goes and drinks in the dish that has been filled by the last shower.

She never drinks a drop of anything but water.

She drinks in little sips, and stretches her neck, balancing herself on the edge of the dish.

Then she hunts around for her scattered food.

The bits of grass are hers, and the insects and the lost seeds.

Tireless, she pecks and pecks.

Now and then, she stops.

Her head upright under its bonnet, her eye bright, her wattles shown off to advantage, she listens first with one ear, then with the other.

Having assured herself that there is nothing new afoot, she goes on with her hunt.

She lifts her stiff legs high, as though she had

the gout. She separates her toes and puts them down carefully without a sound.

She seems to be walking barefoot.

La Dinde

The · Turkey-Hen

1

SHE struts about the barnyard as though we were still under royal rule.

The other fowl do nothing but eat, no matter what. The turkey, between her regular meals, thinks only of looking grand. All her feathers are starched, and the tips of her wings score lines on the ground, as though to mark the path she wishes to follow: this is where she walks, and no other place.

She carries her head too high ever to see her feet.

She hasn't a doubt in the world, and when she sees me approaching, she imagines that I have come to pay my respects.

She starts gobbling with pride.

"Noble turkey," I say, "if you were a goose, I would emulate Buffon and use one of your quills to write your praises. But you are only a turkey."

I must have offended her, because the blood rises to her head. Clusters of wrath hang from her beak. She sees red. With a sharp click, she opens the fan of her tail, and the old sourface turns her back on me.

2

On the road, we meet the turkeys' boarding school.

They go out every day, in any weather.

They are not afraid of the rain, because nobody

knows better than a turkey how to tuck up a skirt; or
of the sun, because a turkey never goes out without
a parasol.

The Birdless Cage

FELIX does not understand how anyone can keep a bird prisoner in a cage.

"Just as," he says, "it is a crime to pick a flower, and, personally, I want to enjoy its scent only when it is still on its stalk, just so are birds made to fly."

Yet he buys a cage; he hangs it in his window. He places in it a nest of wadding, a saucerful of grain, a cup of fresh and renewable water, a swing and a little mirror.

And if, astonished, you question him:

"Every time I look at this cage," he says, "I congratulate myself. I could put a bird in it and I leave it empty. If I wanted to, a brown thrush, or a natty bullfinch, or any of our many birds, would be a slave. Thanks to me, at least one of them is free. That's at least something."

23

The Nest of Goldfinches

THERE was a nest of goldfinches in the forked branch of our cherry tree; pretty to see, round, perfect, all horsehair on the outside and soft down on the inside; and four young goldfinches had just been hatched in it. I said to my father:

"I am tempted to take them and raise them."

My father had often explained to me that it was a crime to cage birds. This time, however, no doubt tired of repeating the same thing, he said nothing. A few days later, I told him:

"If I decide to do it, it will be easy. I'll first put the nest in a cage, and then I'll tie the cage to the cherry tree, and the mother will be able to feed the little ones through the bars until they no longer need her."

My father didn't say what he thought of this scheme.

So I put the nest in a cage and the cage in the cherry tree, and it worked out as I had said: without hesitation, the big goldfinches brought beakfuls of worms to their young. And my father, as entertained as I was, observed from a distance their colorful coming and going, the blood-red and saffron-yellow of their flight.

One evening I said:

"The little ones are now strong enough. If they were free, they'd fly away. I'll let them spend a last night in the family circle, and tomorrow I'll take them into the house and hang the cage in the window. And I'd like you to know that no goldfinches in the world will get better care."

My father said nothing to the contrary.

The next day I found the cage open. My father was there, witnessing my amazement.

"What I'd like to know," I said, "is what idiot went and opened the door of that cage!"

The Cockroach

BLACK and flattened like a keyhole.

The Goose

LIKE the rest of the village girls, Tiennette would like to go to Paris. But is she even capable of minding her geese?

Truth to tell, she follows them rather than leads them. She goes along, behind the troop, mechanically knitting away, and she puts her trust in the goose from Toulouse, who has all the sense of a grown-up person.

The goose from Toulouse knows the way, where good grass is to be found, and when it's time to go home.

As full of courage as the gander is devoid of it, she protects her sisters against the vicious dog. Her neck vibrates and snakes along the ground, then draws itself up, and she dominates the frightened Tiennette. As soon as everything is under control, she is triumphant and sings through her nose that she knows thanks to whom everything is kept in order.

She has no doubt that she could do better still.

And, one evening, she leaves the country.

She goes off along the road, her beak to the wind, her feathers held close. The women she encounters don't dare stop her. She walks at a frightening speed.

And while Tiennette, back there, keeps getting duller and ever more like a goose herself, the goose from Toulouse comes to Paris.

27

La Pintade

The Guinea Hen

SHE is the hunchback of my courtyard. Because of her hump, she dreams only of wounds.

The hens haven't said a word to her: suddenly, she rushes forward and attacks them.

Then she lowers her head, bends her body, and, as fast as her thin legs will carry her, tears off to hit the turkey-hen with her hard beak, right in the middle of her fan.

That show-off was getting on her nerves.

And so, warlike with her blued head and red wattles, she rages from morning till night. She gives battle without reason, perhaps because she always imagines that others are making fun of her size, her bald head, her low tail.

She never ceases piercing the air with her raucous scream.

Sometimes she leaves the barnyard and vanishes. The peaceable fowl have a moment of quiet. But she comes back screeching, and more turbulent than ever. In a frenzy, she wallows on the ground.

What is the matter with her?

The sly old girl has played a trick on me.

She went to lay her egg out in the fields.

I can go hunt for it if I like.

She rolls in the dust, like a hunchback.

The Magpie

SHE always keeps a little leftover snow from the past winter.

Feet together, she hops to the ground; then, in her straight, mechanical flight, makes for a tree.

Sometimes she misses, and can stop only at the next tree.

So common and despised that she seems immortal, wearing formal clothes already in the morning to chatter ceaselessly till evening, insufferable in her white tie and tails, she is the most truly French of our birds.

The Magpie: "Cacacacacaca."
The Frog: "What is she saying?"
The Magpie: "I'm not saying, I'm singing."
The Frog: "Croak!"
The Mole: "Quiet up there, we can't hear ourselves work!"

The Canary

WHAT ever made me buy that bird?

The bird seller told me: "It's a male. Give him a week to get used to his surroundings, and he will sing."

But the bird remains obstinately silent, and does everything wrong.

No sooner have I filled his cup with grain than he attacks it with his beak and scatters it to the four winds.

I tie a cracker between two bars with a string. He eats only the string. He pushes away the cracker and hits it like a hammer, and the cracker falls.

He bathes in his drinking water and drinks out of his bathtub. He distributes droppings equally in both.

He imagines that canary bread is made specially for birds of his kind to nest in, and, following that instinct, he curls up in it.

He hasn't yet learned the use of lettuce leaves and simply tears them up.

When he picks up a seed in all seriousness, with the intention of swallowing it, he is pitiful. He rolls it from one corner of his beak to the other, squeezes and crushes it, and twists his head like a little old man with no teeth left.

His lump of sugar is of no use to him. Is that a stone jutting out, or a balcony, or a not very practical table?

He prefers his tree of little sticks. There are two

that cross, one above the other, and I get sick of watching him jump back and forth on them, with all the mechanical stupidity of a pendulum on a clock that would mark no hours. What fun does he get out of hopping like that? Out of what necessity does he do it?

If he takes a rest from this dull exercise, perched on one foot with a stranglehold on one of the little sticks, he mechanically searches for a hold on the same stick with the other foot.

As soon as winter has come and the stove is lighted, he believes that spring is here, that molting time has come, and he sheds his feathers.

The light from my lamp troubles his nights, throws his sleeping hours out of gear. He goes to bed at nightfall. I let the darkness settle around him. Is he having a dream? Suddenly, I bring the lamp near his cage. He opens his eyes. What! It's already daylight? And at once he starts his activities again, he dances, pecks at a leaf, fans out his tail, stretches his wings.

I blow out the lamp and regret I can't see his bewildered face.

I'm soon tired of that silent bird who lives backward, and I put him out of the window . . . He has no more notion of what to do with liberty than how to use a cage. Somebody will pick him up by hand.

Just don't let them bring him back to me.

Not only do I offer no reward, but I'll swear that I don't know that bird.

Swallows

THEY give me my daily lesson.

They dot the air with tiny cries.

They draw a straight line, put a comma at the end, and, suddenly, start a new paragraph.

They place the house in which I live between wild parentheses.

They rise from the cellar to the roof, too quick for the pond in the garden to get an image of their flight.

With the light pens of their wings, they draw matchless loops and flourishes.

Then, coming together two by two, they join and mix and splash spots of ink on the blue of the sky.

Only the eye of a friend can follow them; you may know Latin and Greek, but I know how to read the Hebrew lettered in the air by the swallows.

The Canary: "I find the swallow stupid: she thinks that a chimney is a tree."

The Bat: "And you can say what you like; of the two of us, she is the one that flies the worse: in broad daylight, she keeps going off in the wrong direction; if she were to fly at night, as I do, she'd be killing herself every minute."

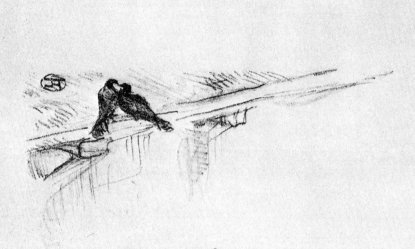

Les Pigeons

The Pigeons

THEY may be making a sound like a muffled drum on the roof;

Or, coming out of the shadows, tumble, burst into the sunlight, and return to the shade;

Or their quick flight may live and die like an opal on a finger;

Or, falling asleep at night in the woods, they may sit so close together that the top branch of the oak is in danger of breaking under that load of painted fruit;

Or, exchanging frenzied curtsies, two of them may become convulsed;

Or one of them may return from afar, bearing a message, and come flying like the thought of the distant sweetheart (Oh! a token dropped!);

Still, all these pigeons, who at first seem entertaining, end by being a bore.

They don't know how to stay in one place, and travel does not broaden them in the least.

All their lives, they remain a bit foolish.

They persist in believing that babies are made through the beak.

And in time you get awfully tired of that hereditary mania for keeping in the throat something that will not go down.

Bats

NIGHT wears itself out through use.

It does not wear out from the top, through its stars. It wears out like a dress dragging on the ground, among stones and trees, down in the depths of unwholesome tunnels and damp caves.

There isn't a corner into which a fragment of night does not penetrate. Thorns pierce it, cold cracks it, mud mars it. And every morning, when night lifts, tatters of it remain caught here and there.

That is how bats are born.

And it is because of these beginnings that they cannot stand the light of day.

After the sun has set and we are outside taking the air, they detach themselves from the old rafters where, lethargic, they have been hanging by a claw.

Their awkward flight fills us with uneasiness. They flutter around us on stiff-veined, featherless wings. They fly by ear rather than with their useless, impaired eyes.

My companion hides her face, and I turn my head away out of fear of an unclean touch.

It is said that, with a greater fervor than we know in love, they would suck our blood until death.

How people exaggerate!

They are harmless. They never touch us.

Daughters of the night, all they hate is light, and all they seek is candles to snuff out with their little funerary shawls.

36

The Wagtail

RUNNING quite as much as flying, always among our feet, familiar and uncatchable, she dares us, with her little cries, to step on her tail.

Le

Paon

The Peacock

HE must certainly be getting married today.

It was supposed to have been yesterday. He was ready, dressed in his grandest cl. hes. He was only waiting for his betrothed. She didn't come. She can't be long now.

Full of glory, bearing himself like an Indian prince, he walks along wearing about his person the rich gifts that custom dictates. Love lends a glow to his colors and his crown trembles like a lyre.

The betrothed does not come.

He climbs to the roof and looks toward the sun. He gives his satanic cry:

"Léon! Léon!"

That is how he calls his betrothed. He sees nothing coming and nobody answers. The barnyard fowl are used to him and don't so much as lift their heads. They are tired of admiring him. He descends again to the yard, so sure of his beauty that he can bear no grudges.

His wedding will be for tomorrow.

And, not knowing what to do with the rest of the day, he walks up to the terrace. He takes the stairs at a ceremonial gait, as though they were the steps of a temple.

He raises his train, weighted down with all the eyes that haven't been able to tear themselves away from it.

And, once more, he rehearses the ceremony.

The Oriole

I tell him:

> "Give back that cherry, right away."

> "All right," replies the oriole.

He gives back the cherry and, along with the cherry, the three hundred thousand grubs of harmful insects he swallows in a year.

Grackle!

THERE is an old walnut tree in my garden, almost dead, and frightening to the little birds. A blackbird lives alone among its last few leaves.

But the rest of the garden is full of flowering trees in whose young branches lively birds of all colors have their nests.

The young trees seem to make fun of the old walnut. At every moment, they can be seen hurling at it a flight of chattering birds, like a handful of teasing words.

Sparrows, martins, titmice, and canaries take turns at tormenting it. They knock the tips of its branches with their wings. The air crackles with their tiny cries; then they flee, and another pestering band escapes from the young trees, mocking, twittering, whistling, singing itself hoarse.

So, from dawn to dusk, like bursts of jeering words, canaries, titmice, martins, and sparrows break out of the young trees and at the old one.

And sometimes the old one loses patience, stirs those last few leaves, releases its blackbird, and replies:

"Gr-r-rackle!"

The Jay: "Ugly grackle, always dressed in black!"
The Grackle: "Mr. Administrator, I have nothing else to wear."

41

The Lark

I HAVE never seen a lark, and it's useless for me to get up at dawn. The lark does not belong to the earth.

Since early morning, I have been treading over lumps of earth and dry grass.

Bands of gray sparrows and brightly painted gold-finches hover over the thorn hedges.

The jay, in official garb, passes the trees in review.

A quail skims the clover, on a line of flight that seems marked out with a ruler.

Behind the shepherd who knits better than a woman, sheep, all alike, follow each other.

And everything is full of a light so new that you smile at the ill-omened crow.

But listen as I am listening.

Do you hear, some place up there, bits of crystal being broken up in a golden bowl?

Who can tell where the lark is singing?

If I look up into the air, the sun singes my eyes.

I'll have to give up trying to see him.

The lark lives in the sky; and he is the only bird belonging to the sky whose song reaches us.

The Squirrel

A plume! A fine plume! Yes, certainly, but, my dear little friend, that's not where you're supposed to wear it.

Le
Cygne

The Swan

HE glides over the pond like a white sleigh, going from cloud to cloud. Because all he is hungry for is those flaky clouds that he sees coming into being, moving, and losing themselves in the water. It's one of those he wants. Aiming for it with his beak, he plunges into it his snow-clad neck.

Then, like a woman's arm coming out of a sleeve, he draws it out.

He has nothing.

He looks: the clouds have taken fright and have disappeared.

He remains undeceived only a short while, because the clouds are soon back, and over there, where the ripples are dying out in the water, you can see one taking shape again.

Gently, on his light pillow of down, the swan swims up to it . . .

He exhausts himself trying to fish for empty reflections, and perhaps he will die, a victim of his illusion, before he catches a single piece of cloud.

But what am I saying?

Every time he dives, his beak digs into the nourishing mud of the bottom and brings back a worm.

He is getting fat as a goose.

45

The Kingfisher

THIS evening nothing would bite, but I bring home a rare and moving experience.

As I was holding out my fishing rod, a kingfisher came and perched on it.

We have no more brilliantly colored bird.

He looked like a big blue flower at the end of a long stem. The rod bent under his weight. I hardly dared breathe, full of pride as I was at being taken for a tree by a kingfisher.

I'm sure it was not out of fear that he flew away: he just thought he was going from one branch to another.

46

The Whale

WITH her mouthful of whalebone, she should be able to make herself a corset; although, with that waist measurement! . . .

The Gudgeon

HE swims up the current of the brook, following the line of stones: he does not care for either mud or grass.

He catches sight of a bottle lying on a bed of sand. It contains nothing but water. I purposely forgot to put bait in it. The gudgeon swims around it, looks for the entrance, and is caught.

I bring in the bottle and throw him back.

A little further upstream, he hears something. Far from fleeing, full of curiosity, he comes nearer. It's me, trampling around in the water and stirring up the bottom with a stick at the edge of a net. The gudgeon insists upon trying to go through a loop. He stays in it.

I raise the net and throw him back.

Further down, a sudden jerk stretches my fishing line, and the bicolored floater sinks beneath the water.

I draw it out and it's the gudgeon again.

I take him off the hook and throw him in.

This time I won't get him back.

He is there, motionless, in the clear water at my feet. I can make out his wide head, his big, stupid eye, his pair of whiskers.

He yawns with his torn lip, and he is panting from the scare he's had.

But nothing cures him.

I drop my line in again, with the same worm.

And right away the gudgeon bites again.

Which one of us will be the first to give up?

Definitely, they've made up their minds not to bite.
Don't they know that the fishing season opened today?

Le Chien

The Dog

WE can't put Pointu outside in this weather. The wind whistles so sharply under the door that he even has to leave the doormat. He looks around for something better and pushes his good-natured head between our seats. But we sit bent toward the fire, elbow to elbow, and I give Pointu a slap. My father pushes him away with his foot. Mother calls him names. My sister offers him an empty glass.

Pointu sneezes and goes out to the kitchen to see if anyone is there.

Then he comes back, forces his way through our circle at the risk of getting strangled by knees, and there he is, in a corner of the fireplace.

After turning about for a long time, he sits down next to the andiron and stays put. He looks so gently at his masters that we let him be. Only, the andiron is almost red-hot and the ashes burn his backside.

Still, he stays.

We open a passage for him:

"There, get out! My, you're stupid!"

He persists, however. At a time when the teeth of the stray dogs are grating with the cold, Pointu, in his warm corner, his fur singed, his behind cooked, holds back his howls and laughs out of the wrong side of his mouth with eyes full of tears.

The Cat

MINE does not eat mice; he doesn't care for them. He catches them just for something to play with.

When he has played all he wants, he grants the mouse its life, and goes off innocently to dream elsewhere, seated in the ring of his tail, his head closed up like a fist.

But, because of those claws, the mouse is dead.

The Flea

A speck of tobacco with a spring in it.

Le Bœuf

The Ox

THE door opens this morning as usual, and Castor, without a stumble, goes out of the barn. In slow draughts, he drinks his share of the water in the trough, leaving the share of belated Pollux. Then, his nose dripping like a tree after a downpour, he goes willingly, weightily, and in good order, to his habitual place under the yoke of the cart.

His horns bound, his head motionless, he wrinkles his belly, languidly switches his tail at the black flies, and, like a maidservant dozing on her broom, chews his cud while waiting for Pollux.

In the court, however, the farm hands are rushing around, shouting and swearing, and the dog barks as though scenting the approach of a stranger.

Can this be the placid Pollux, for the first time in his life resisting the goad, and twisting around, bumping into Castor's side, fuming, and, when finally harnessed, trying to throw off the yoke they share?

No, it is another.

Castor, unpaired, stops the motion of his jaws when his eye encounters, close to his, the turbid eye of an ox he does not know.

At sunset, the oxen slowly drag through the fields the light harrow of their shadow.

Le Taureau

The Bull

SKIPPING his green fly over the water, the fisherman steps lightly along the bank of the river Yonne.

He catches the green flies on the trunks of poplars polished by cattle rubbing against them.

He casts his line with a sharp snap, and draws it in with assurance.

He is sure that each new spot is the best one yet; and pretty soon he leaves it, swings his leg over a fence, and passes over into the next field.

Suddenly, as he is crossing a wide field that burns in the sun, he stops.

Over on the far side, in the midst of peaceful, reclining cows, the bull has just ponderously gotten to his feet.

It is a famous bull, whose size surprises the people passing on the road. He is admired from a distance and, if he hasn't already done it, he could quite well hurl a man into the air like an arrow, with the bow of his horns. Gentle as a lamb when he feels like it, he is at times seized by rages, and if you are in his vicinity at the time, there is no telling what may happen.

The fisherman watches him obliquely.

"If I run," he thinks, "the bull will be upon me before I get out of the field. If I jump in the river, not being able to swim, I'll drown. If I lie down and play dead, they say the bull will sniff me and not hurt me. Are they sure of that? And suppose he should not go away, what agony! Better pretend I don't care."

57

And the fisherman continues to fish as though the bull were not there. He hopes, that way, to put him off.

The back of his neck is burning under his straw hat.

He restrains his feet, which are aching to run, and forces them to take their time over the grass. Heroically, he dips his green fly in the water. He only hides now and then, behind the poplars. In a leisurely way, he reaches the fence in the hedge where, with a last effort of his worn-out limbs, he will be able to leap, safe and sound, out of the field.

But why all this haste?

The bull, paying no attention to him, stays with the cows.

He has risen to his feet just to move a little, out of weariness, the way one stretches oneself.

He turns his curly head into the evening wind.

At intervals, with eyes half-closed, he bellows.

He bellows languidly, and listens to his bellowing.

The women know him by the curly hair on his forehead.

The Cow

TIRED of casting around for a name, we have ended by not giving her one.

We call her simply "the cow," and it is the name that suits her best.

Besides, what does it matter, provided she eats!

And as for fresh grass, dry hay, vegetables, grain, even bread and salt, she has as much as she wants of everything, and she eats everything, all the time, twice over, since she chews her cud.

Whenever she sees me, she comes running at a light little trot on split hoofs, her hide stretched over her feet like white stockings; she comes entirely certain that I am bringing something that can be eaten. And, while admiring her each time, all I can say is: "There, eat!"

Out of what she absorbs she makes milk, not fat. At a set hour, she presents us with her full, square udder. She does not hold back her milk—there are some cows that do—generously, through her four elastic teats, which hardly need pressing, she empties her fountain. She does not move a foot or a tail, but, with her supple, enormous tongue, diverts herself by licking the back of the milking woman.

Although she lives alone, her appetite keeps her from being bored. It seldom happens that she lets out a moo in vague remembrance of her last calf. But she is fond of visitors, and receives graciously, with her horns raised above her brow, and eager lips from which hang a thread of water and a bit of grass.

The men, who fear nothing, stroke her outjutting belly; the women, surprised that an animal so large can be so gentle, remain wary only of her endearments, and daydream happily over her.

She likes to have me scratch her between the horns. I back away a bit as her eagerness brings her closer, and the good big beast keeps this up until I have put my foot in her dung.

The Rain Flies

THERE is only one oak tree in the middle of the field, and the oxen occupy all the shade of its leaves.

With lowered heads, they turn impassive horns toward the sun.

They'd be comfortable if it weren't for the flies.

But today, truly, the flies are voracious. Acrid and numerous, the black ones stick like scabs of soot to the eyes, the nostrils, even to the corners of the mouth, while the green ones have a preference for the latest scratch in the hide.

When an ox moves his leather apron or stamps on the dry earth, the swarms rise, murmuring. They seem to be fermenting.

It is so hot that, on their doorsteps, the old women scent the storm and are already making their frightened jokes:

"Beware of the *bourdoudou!*" they say.

In the distance, a luminous spear noiselessly pierces the sky. A drop of rain falls.

The oxen, alerted, raise their heads, move to the edge of the oak tree, and puff in patience.

They know what is coming: good flies to drive away the bad ones.

At first singly, then close together, they come down from the tattered sky, upon an enemy that slowly gives way and disperses.

Before long, from stubby nose to durable tail, the streaming oxen are rippling with well-being under the victorious swarm of the flies of rain.

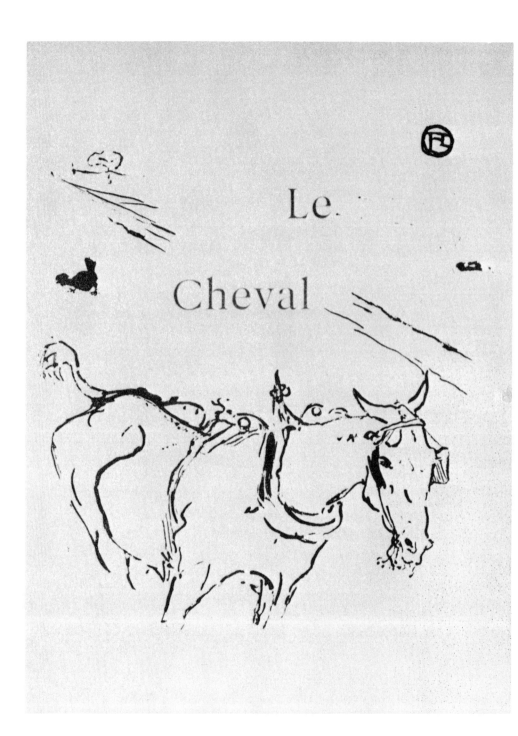

Le.

Cheval

The Horse

THAT horse of mine is far from handsome. He has too many knobs and hollows, and he has flat ribs, a rat's tail, and the incisors of an Englishwoman. But I find him touching. I can't get over the fact that he remains in my service and, without rebelling, allows himself to be turned this way and that.

Every time I put on his harness, I expect him to motion roughly, *no,* and bolt.

He does nothing of the kind. He lowers and raises his big head as though he were straightening a hat, and backs submissively into his shafts.

And so I am not sparing with his oats and corn. I brush him until he glistens like a cherry. I comb his mane, I braid his thin tail. I stroke him and speak to him. I sponge his eyes. I polish his hoofs.

Does all that mean anything to him?

You can't tell.

He farts.

I admire him particularly when he takes me around in the buggy. I whip him up and he quickens his gait. I stop him and he stops me. I pull the rein to the left and he goes to the left, instead of hauling off to the right and dumping me into the ditch with his hoofs you know where.

I am afraid of him and sorry for him, and he makes me feel ashamed.

Isn't he soon going to wake up from that half-sleep

of his and, taking my place with due authority, put me down in his?

What does he think about?

He farts, farts, farts.

The Death of Brunette

As he wakes me Philippe tells me that he had gotten up in the night to listen to her, and that she seemed to be breathing quietly.

But, since this morning, she worries him.

He gives her dry hay and she refuses it.

He offers her a little fresh grass, and Brunette, usually so eager, hardly touches it. She no longer looks at her calf; and she seems to be sensitive to his nose-bumps when he stands up on his stiff legs to suck.

Philippe separates them and ties the calf far from his mother. Brunette does not appear to notice.

Philippe's anxiety is infecting us all. Even the children want to get up.

The veterinarian arrives, examines Brunette and takes her out of the barn. She knocks against the wall and stumbles over the threshold. She almost falls: we have to take her in again.

"She's a very sick cow," the vet says.

We don't dare ask what is wrong with her.

He fears milk fever, which is often fatal, especially in good milkers. Recalling, one after another, those that had been believed lost and that he had saved, he takes out a bottle of liquid and, with a paint-brush, he spreads its contents over Brunette's ribs.

"It will act as a vesicatory," he says. "I don't know its exact composition. It comes from Paris. If the disease does not reach the brain, she will pull out of it; otherwise, I'll use the ice-water method. It surprises simple peasants, but I know what I'm doing."

"Go ahead, Monsieur."

Brunette, lying on the straw, can still hold up the weight of her head. She stops chewing her cud. She seems to be holding her breath in order to hear what is going on inside of her.

We wrap her in a wool blanket, because her ears and horns are growing cold.

"As long as the ears don't flop," Philippe says, "there is hope."

Twice, she tries in vain to stand up. She is taking heavy breaths, farther and farther apart.

And now she lets her head drop on her left flank.

"It's getting bad," Philippe says, squatting beside her and murmuring pet names.

She raises her head and drops it against the edge of the manger, with a muffled blow so heavy that we exclaim.

We tuck a lot of straw around her so that she won't knock herself out.

She stretches her neck and legs, and spreads out full length, as she did in the pasture when a storm was brewing.

The vet decides to bleed her. He doesn't come too close. He is supposed to know as much as the next one, but to be less bold than most.

With the first blows of the wooden hammer, the lancet slides over the vein. After a more assured stroke, the blood gushes into the tin bucket that is usually filled to the brim with milk.

To stop the flow, the vet closes the vein with a steel pin.

Then, from Brunette's brow to her tail, we apply a sheet dipped in well water and we change it often, because it heats up quickly. She doesn't even shiver. Philippe holds her firmly by the horns to keep her head from hitting her left side.

Brunette, as though subjugated, doesn't move any more. We can't tell whether she is getting better or worse.

We are all sad, but Philippe's sadness has the dull mournfulness of an animal watching another animal suffer.

His wife brings him his morning soup, and he eats it without relish, sitting on a stool, and doesn't finish it.

"It's the end," he says. "Brunette is swelling."

At first we don't believe him, but Philippe is right. She is swelling visibly, and the swelling doesn't go down, as though the air that comes in can't get out again.

Philippe's wife asks:

"Is she dead?"

"Don't you see?" Philippe says harshly.

Mme. Philippe goes out into the yard.

"It will be a long time before I go looking for another one," Philippe says.

"Another what?"

"Another Brunette."

"You'll go when I want you to," I say in a masterful tone that surprises me.

We try to make ourselves believe that the accident annoys us more than it grieves us, and already we are saying that Brunette has croaked.

But that evening, I met the church bell-ringer on

the street, and I don't know what kept me from saying to him:

"Here are five francs, go ring the knell for someone that's died in my house."

The Lizard

SPONTANEOUSLY born of the cracked stone against which I am leaning, he climbs on my shoulder. He thinks I am part of the wall because I am motionless and my coat is the color of stone. When all is said and done, it is flattering.

> *The Wall:* "Some sort of shudder is running across my back."
> *The Lizard:* "It's me."

The Ants

Every one of them looks like the numeral 3. And what scads and scads of them there are! There are 333333333333 . . . to infinity.

The Ant and the Partridge

An ant had fallen into a rut full of rain water and was about to drown, when a young partridge, who happened to be drinking there, picked her out with his beak and saved her.

"I'll do the same for you some day," said the ant.

The partridge was skeptical. "We are no longer in the days of La Fontaine," he said. "Not that I doubt your gratefulness, but how would you go about pricking the heel of a hunter who was ready to shoot me? Nowadays hunters don't walk barefoot."

The ant didn't stay to argue the point, but hurried off to catch up with her sisters, who all go the same way, like black beads being strung.

The hunter was not far away.

He was resting, lying on his side under a tree. He caught sight of the partridge tripping about and picking in the stubble. He sat up and wanted to reach for his rifle, but his right arm was asleep. It felt full of ants. He couldn't raise it, and meanwhile the partridge did not wait for the ants to go away.

L'Ane

The Donkey

HE doesn't care about a thing. Every morning, with the quick, sharp little step of a government clerk, he takes around the delivery agent Jacquot, who distributes in the villages articles obtained in town—groceries, bread, meat, a few newspapers, a letter.

The round of distribution finished, Jacquot and the donkey work for themselves. The buggy is used as a cart. They go together to the vineyard, to the woods, to the potato fields. They bring back at times vegetables, at times green brushwood, either that or something else, depending on the day.

Jacquot never stops saying "Giddap! Giddap!" to no purpose, as he might snore. Sometimes the donkey, because he smells a thistle or is hit by an idea, stops. Jacquot puts an arm around his neck and pushes. If the donkey resists, Jacquot bites his ear.

They eat in the ditches, the master a crust of bread and onions, the beast whatever he wants to.

They only start home by nightfall. Their shadows move slowly from one tree to the next.

All of a sudden, the lake of silence in which things lie bathed and already asleep cracks open in turmoil.

What housewife can, at this hour, be turning her rusty and screeching windlass to draw water out of her well?

It's the donkey going home and, throwing his entire voice to the winds, braying, to extinction, that he doesn't give a damn, he doesn't give a damn.

DONKEY

The rabbit, grown up.

The Worm

THERE's one that stretches and drags itself out like a fine noodle!

The Snake

Too long.

The Garden Snake

WHAT belly did that long ache drop from?

Le Cochon

The Hog

GROUCHY, but familiar as though we had minded you together, you poke your snout everywhere, and you walk with it as much as you do with your feet.

You hide your little currant eyes under beetroot-leaf ears.

Your belly is swollen like a gooseberry.

Like the gooseberry, you have long hairs, a light skin, and a short, curly tail.

And mean people call you: "Dirty hog!"

They say you turn up your nose at nothing, but you turn everybody's stomach, and that you only like to drink greasy dishwater.

They slander you.

Let them wash you and you will look fine.

It's their fault if you neglect yourself.

As they make your bed you must lie in it, and dirt is only your second nature.

The Pig and the Pearls

As soon as he is let out in the fields, the pig begins to eat, and his snout never leaves the ground.

He does not select the fine grass. He goes at the first grass that comes along and pushes his tireless snout in front of him, any way, like a plowshare or a blind mole.

His only preoccupation is to round off his belly, which is already taking on the shape of the salting barrel, and he is never bothered by the weather.

He doesn't mind in the least that his silky bristles almost caught fire a while ago under the noon sun, and it doesn't matter, either, if that heavy cloud, swollen with hailstones, bursts and breaks over the field.

The magpie departs in her mechanical flight; the turkeys hide under the hedge; and the callow colt takes shelter under an oak tree.

But the pig stays where he is eating.

He doesn't miss a mouthful.

His tail wiggles with not a bit less contentment.

Spattered with hail, he barely takes the time to grumble:

"More of their darn pearls!"

The Weasel

Poor, but neat, refined, she crosses and recrosses the road in little jumps as she goes from ditch to ditch and hole to hole on her round of private lessons.

Les

Moutons

The Sheep

THEY are returning from the stubble, where, since morning, they have been grazing with their noses in the shadow of their bodies.

Following signals from the lazy shepherd, the dog goes after the flock wherever necessary.

It fills the entire road, waving from one ditch to the other and running over; or, piled together, forms a soft mass, trampling the ground with the tripping steps of old women. When it begins to run, the feet make a noise like rushes, and riddle the dust of the road in a honeycomb pattern.

One sheep, curly, nicely garnished, jumps like a bale thrown in the air, and sprays pellets.

Another feels dizzy, and his head, badly screwed on, hits his knee.

They invade the village. One would think this was their feast-day, and that, saucily, they were bleating their joy through the streets.

But they don't stop in the village, and I see them reappear over there, going toward the horizon. Over the hill, they climb lightly toward the sun. Having approached it, they lie down at a distance . . .

Stragglers take on an unexpected last shape against the sky, and catch up with the cottony flock.

One flake separates itself from the rest and floats, like white moss, then becomes smoke, then steam, and then nothing.

Only a leg is left out.

It stretches out, thins out like a distaff, to infinity.

The chilly sheep go to sleep around the weary sun who, undoing his crown, sticks his rays into their wool until tomorrow.

The Sheep: "Buh . . . buh . . . buh . . ."
The Dog: "But me no buts!"

The Glowworm

WHAT's going on? Nine o'clock at night and his light is still on!

The Wasp

She is sure to end by ruining her figure.

The Dragonfly

SHE is nursing a case of pinkeye.

Moving from one side of the stream to the other, she spends her time bathing her swollen eyes in the cool water.

And she crackles as though she were flying by electricity.

Le

Bouc

The Billy Goat

His smell precedes him. Long before he is seen, it is there.

He advances at the head of the herd, which follows him helter-skelter, in a cloud of dust.

His fur is long, dry hair, parted down his back.

He is prouder of his size than he is of his beard, because the nanny-goat, too, wears a beard under her chin.

When he passes, some hold their noses; others enjoy that savor.

He looks neither to the right nor to the left; he walks stiffly, his ears pointed and his tail short. If men have loaded their sins upon him, he knows nothing about it, and, gravely, he drops a rosary of dung.

Alexander is his name, known even to the dogs.

The day over, the sun set, he returns to the village with the harvesters. His horns, bent with age, have gradually taken on the shape of sickles.

The Cricket

I⊤ is the hour when, tired of straying around, the blackamoor insect has returned from his outing and carefully repairs the disorder in his domain.

First he rakes the narrow sand paths.

He makes sawdust and spreads it in front of his retreat.

He files down the root of that long blade of grass that might conceivably attack him.

He takes a rest.

Then he winds his tiny watch.

Has he finished? Is it broken? He takes another little rest.

He goes into his house and closes his door.

For a long time, he turns the key in the delicate keyhole.

Then he listens:

There is no alarm outside.

But he doesn't feel quite safe.

And, as though letting out a little chain on a grinding winch, he goes deep down into the earth.

We hear nothing more.

In the silent countryside, the poplars stand like fingers pointing at the moon.

90

The Grasshopper

COULD he be the game warden among insects?

All day long he jumps about in furious pursuit of invisible poachers, never caught.

The tallest grasses don't stop him.

He is afraid of nothing, because he has seven-league boots, the neck of a bull, the brow of a genius, the belly of a ship, celluloid wings, devil's horns, and a big sword on his backside.

But one can't have the virtues of a game warden without having his faults; and it should be told: the grasshopper chews tobacco.

If you think I'm lying, follow him with your fingers, play puss-in-the-corner with him, and when you have caught him as, between two leaps, he sits on a blade of clover, observe his mouth: between his terrible mandibles, he secretes a black foam like tobacco juice.

But you've already lost him. His jumping fury has taken hold of him again. In a sudden effort, the green monster has escaped you, and, since he is fragile and can be taken apart, he has left a little leg in your hand.

Les

Lapins

The Rabbits

In their half-barrel, Black and Gray, their paws warm under their fur, they eat like cows. They have only one meal, which lasts all day.

If fresh grass is slow in coming to them, they gnaw the old down to the roots, and even the roots keep their teeth busy.

A head of lettuce has just fallen to them. Black and Gray attack it together.

Nose to nose, they work away, and their heads nod, and their ears trot.

When only one leaf is left, each seizes one edge, and they have a speed contest.

They look as though they were playing, even if they don't laugh, and you think that once the leaf is finished, a brotherly fondness will bring their noses together.

But Gray is weakening. Since yesterday, he has a swollen belly, and is bloated by a water pocket. Truly, he was stuffing himself too much. Even though a lettuce leaf can go down without your being really hungry, he can't go on. He lets go of the leaf and lies down on his side, on top of his droppings, with short convulsions.

He lies rigid, his legs apart, like an advertisement for firearms: *We kill cleanly, we kill far.*

For a moment, Black, surprised, stops eating. Sitting up like a candlestick, his breath gentle, his lips together, his eye circled in pink, he looks.

He resembles a sorcerer about to penetrate a mystery.

His two erect ears mark the last, solemn moment.

Then they break.

He finishes the lettuce leaf.

The Vineyard

ALL the vines, their props upright, are presenting arms.

What are they expecting? There will be no more grapes this year, and vine leaves are no longer used in anything but statues.

In the Garden

The Spade: "Fac et spera."
The Pick: "Me too."

The Flowers: "Will it be sunny today?"
The Sunflower: "Yes, if I want it to be."
The Watering Can: "Excuse me, if I want, it will
   rain, and if I remove my nozzle, it will rain
   in torrents."

The Rosebush: "Oh! What a wind!"
The Trellis: "I'm here."

The Raspberry: "Why do roses have thorns? You
   can't eat a rose."
The Carp in the Pond: "Well said! It is because
   they eat me that I prick them with my bones."
The Thistle: "Yes, but too late."

The Rose: "Do you think I'm beautiful?"
The Bumble Bee: "I'd have to see your under-
   things."
The Rose: "Come in."

96

The Bee: "On with it! Everybody says I'm a good worker. By the end of the month I should be promoted to department head."

The Violets: "We're all officers of the Academy."
The White Violets: "One more reason for being modest, my sisters."
The Leek: "No doubt. Do I brag?"

The Spinach: "It's I who am the sorrel."
The Sorrel: "Why no, I am."

The Onion: "My! What an awful smell!"
The Garlic: "I bet it's that carnation again."

The Asparagus: "My little finger tells me all."

The Potato: "I think I've just had babies."

Apple Tree, to the Pear Tree facing it: "It's your pear, your pear, your pear . . . It's your pear I'd like to yield."

La Souris

The Mouse

As I write my daily pages by the light of a lamp, I hear a light noise. If I stop, it ceases. It begins again as soon as I start scratching the paper.

It's a mouse waking up.

I sense her comings and goings at the edge of the dark recess in which our maid keeps her cleaning rags and brushes.

She jumps to the floor and scampers over the kitchen tiles. She passes near the fireplace, under the sink, loses herself among the dishes, and, by a series of reconnaissances which she pushes farther and farther, she moves nearer to me.

Every time I lay down my pen, the silence worries her. Every time I use it, she probably thinks there is another mouse somewhere around, and feels reassured.

Then I don't see her anymore. She is under my table, between my feet. She circulates from one chair leg to another. She touches my wooden shoes, gnaws one slightly; and, boldly, there she is on top!

And I must not move my leg or breathe too freely: she'd bolt.

But I must continue to write; out of fear that she will abandon me to my loneliness, I scribble little signs, anything, tiny, tiny marks, resembling her nibblings.

99

Monkeys...

Go look at the monkeys (bad boys, they've all torn the seat of their pants!) climbing, dancing in the new sun, losing their tempers, scratching themselves, peeling things, and drinking with a primitive grace, while their eyes, dulled at times but not for long, give out quickly extinguished sparks.

Go look at the flamingoes, walking on fire tongs for fear of wetting their pink petticoats in the pond; the swans and the vain plumbing of their necks; the ostrich with the wings of a chick and the visored cap of a responsible stationmaster; the storks who keep shrugging their shoulders (so that in the end it means nothing); the marabou shivering in his poor little jacket; the penguins in their short capes; the pelican carrying his beak as though it were a wooden sword; and the parakeets, the tamest of which are not as tame as their keeper, who ended by taking a half-franc piece out of my hand.

Go see the yak heavy with prehistoric thoughts; the giraffe who shows us, above the bars of her fence, her head at the end of a pike; the elephant, bent over, his nose to the ground, dragging his socks in front of his door: he almost disappears into the sack of pants pulled up too high, and on which, behind, a little rope hangs.

Do go and see the porcupine decorated with penholders that must be most inconvenient for him and his girl-friend; the zebra, exact reproduction of every other zebra; the panther, who has come down to the foot of his bed; the bear who amuses us and is not amused; and the lion, yawning until we, too, yawn.

End of the Hunting Season

Iт's a poor day, gray and short, as though gnawed at both ends.

Toward noon, a sulky sun tries to get through the fog and half opens a pale eye that it immediately closes again.

I walk aimlessly. My rifle is of no use to me, and my dog, usually so frisky, sticks close to me.

The water in the river is so clear it hurts: if you dipped your fingers into it, it would cut like broken glass.

In the stubble, a sluggish lark bursts out at each one of my steps. They come together, whirl around, and their flight hardly disturbs the frozen air.

Farther off, congregations of crows dig up the autumn grain with their beaks.

Three partridges stand up in the middle of the field, whose close-cropped grass no longer protects them.

How big they are! They're grown-up ladies now. Worried, they listen. I've seen them all right, but I leave them alone and go away. And some place, no doubt, a trembling hare feels reassured and puts his nose outside his hole.

All along this hedge (here and there a last leaf beats its wing like a bird with a foot caught in a trap) a blackbird flees at my approach, goes and hides a little way off, then comes out under the nose of the dog and, at no risk to himself, makes fun of us.

Gradually, the fog thickens. I could believe I am lost. In my hands, my rifle is nothing but a stick that could explode. From whence comes that vague noise, that sheep's bleat, that sound of a bell, that human cry?

Time to go home. Over an already obliterated road, I return to the village. It alone knows its name. It is inhabited by humble peasants, and no one comes to see it but me.

L'Escargot

The Snail

IN the season of colds, the snail stays at home and, its giraffe neck pulled in, boils like a full nose.

On fine days it goes for rambles, but it can only walk on its tongue.

2

My friend Abel was playing with his snails.

He is raising a boxful of them, and, in order to tell them apart, he marks a number on each shell, in pencil.

If the weather is too dry, the snails sleep in their box. As soon as rain threatens, Abel lines them up outside, and, if the rain is late, he wakes them up by pouring a pot of water over them. And all, says he, except the mothers brooding at the bottom of the box, are under the keeping of a dog named Barbare, who is a strip of lead that Abel pushes along with his finger.

As I was discussing with him the work entailed in raising snails, I noticed that he was motioning *no,* even while he was saying *yes.*

"Abel," I said, "why does your head move that way from right to left?"

"It's my sugar," Abel said.

"What sugar?"

"See, here."

As, on all fours, he was bringing back the number 8 which was about to stray, I saw, on Abel's neck, between his skin and his shirt, a lump of sugar hanging on a thread, like a medal.

"Mother hangs it on me," he said, "when she wants to punish me."

"Does it bother you?"

"Well, it scratches."

"And it stings, huh? The skin is all red."

"But when I'm forgiven," Abel said, "I eat it."

The Caterpillar

HE comes out of a clump of grass that hid him during the heat of day. He crosses the sandy path in great undulations. He is careful not to stop, and for a moment he believes himself lost in the track made by the gardener's wooden shoe.

Having arrived at the strawberry patch, he takes a rest and lifts his nose, sniffing to the right and to the left; then he's off again and, over the leaves, under the leaves, he knows now where he's going.

What a beautiful caterpillar, fat, velvety, furred, brown with golden spots and black eyes!

Guided by his sense of smell, he quivers and frowns like a thick eyebrow.

He stops at the foot of a rosebush.

He tests the tough skin with his delicate cramp-irons, waves his little newborn pup's head, and decides to make the ascent.

And, this time, you'd think he was swallowing each length of the way in a laborious gulp.

At the very top of the bush, there blooms a rose with the complexion of an ingenuous little girl. She is intoxicated with her own scent. She mistrusts no one. The first caterpillar who wishes to do so may climb up her stem. She receives him as though he were a present.

And, since she has a feeling that the coming night will be chilly, she is happy to have a furry boa to put around her neck.

The Butterfly

A billet-doux folded in half and hunting for the address of a flower.

The Frogs

THEY uncoil their springs in sudden leaps.

They jump up from the grass like heavy drops of frying oil.

They settle down, like bronze paper weights, on the wide leaves of the water lily.

One of them is gulping air. You feel like putting a coin in his mouth for the penny bank in his belly.

They come up from the ooze like sighs.

Motionless, they resemble bulging eyes at water level, tumors on the flat pond.

Sitting cross-legged and stupefied, they yawn at the setting sun.

Then, like newsboys filling the street with noise, they cry out the last news of the day.

They're having a party this evening: do you hear them rinsing their glasses?

Now and then they snap up an insect.

And others among them think only of love.

And all of them tempt the fisherman.

I break off a stick without trouble. I have a pin stuck in my coat, and I bend it into a hook.

I have plenty of string.

But I would need a scrap of yarn, a bit of anything red.

I search on myself, on the ground, in the sky.

I find nothing, and I look sadly at my empty buttonhole, ready and waiting for the red ribbon of the Legion of Honor.

Le Crapaud

The Toad

Born of a stone, he lives under a stone and will dig his grave in one.

I visit him often, and every time I lift away his stone, I am afraid of finding him, and afraid he may no longer be there.

He is there.

Hidden in that clean, dry refuge, narrow and his very own, he occupies it fully, blown up like a miser's purse.

If rain makes him emerge, he comes to meet me. After a few heavy jumps, he rests on his haunches and looks at me with his reddened eyes.

An unjust world may treat him like a leper, but I am not afraid of squatting down and putting my human face near his.

Then I'll overcome a remaining particle of repulsion and, toad, I'll stroke you with my hand!

In life we are called upon to swallow more sickening ones.

Still, yesterday, I was lacking in tact. He was fermenting and sweating out of all his broken warts.

"My poor friend," I said, "I don't want to hurt your feelings, but, heavens, you're ugly!"

He opened his childish, toothless mouth, breathing hot, and replied, with a slight English accent:

"What about you?"

III

The Woodcock

ALL that was left of the April sun was a pink glimmer on the clouds, motionless as though they had arrived at destination.

In the narrow clearing where my father was waiting for the woodcocks, night rose from the ground and little by little clothed us.

Standing near him, I could discern clearly only his face. Taller than I, he hardly saw me; and the dog could be heard panting, invisible at our feet.

The thrushes were hurrying back to the woods, and the blackbird was giving his guttural cry, that sort of neigh which is an order to all birds to hush up and go to sleep.

The woodcock would soon leave his retreat of dead leaves and rise. When the weather is mild, as it was that evening, he hangs back before going out into open country. He turns back to the woods and looks for a companion. You can tell, from his light call, whether he is drawing nearer or moving on. He passes in a heavy flight between the big oaks, and his long beak hangs so low that he seems to be walking with a little cane.

As I was listening and looking around in every direction, my father suddenly fired; but he did not follow the dog's forward dash.

"You missed it?" I said.

"I didn't fire," he said. "The gun went off in my hands."

"All by itself?"

"Yes."

"Oh! . . . could it have been a bough?"

"I don't know."

I could hear him taking out the empty shell.

"How were you holding it?"

Didn't he understand?

"I mean, in what direction was the barrel pointing?"

As he had stopped answering, I didn't dare say anything more. Finally I told him:

"You might have killed . . . the dog."

"Let's get out of here," my father said.

L'Araignée

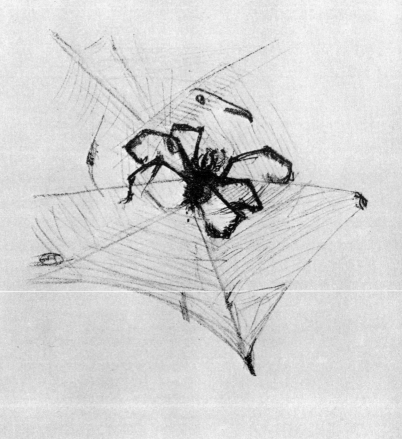

The Spider

A little hand, hairy and black, clutching hairs.

All night long, in the name of the moon, she affixes her seals.

The Poppies

THEY burst in the midst of the wheat like an army of small soldiers, although of a much richer red; and there is no harm in them.

Their sword is a blade of wheat.

It's the wind that makes them run, and any poppy, when he wants to, may linger along the edge of a furrow with his girl-friend, the cornflower.

The Partridges

THE partridge and the plowman live in peace, he behind his plow, she in the neighboring clover, just the right distance apart so as not to get in each other's way. The partridge knows the plowman's voice: he doesn't frighten her when he shouts or swears.

If the plow screaks or the ox coughs or the donkey brays, she knows it means nothing.

This peace lasts until I disturb it.

I arrive on the scene, and the partridge flies off, the plowman is worried, and so are the ox and the donkey. I fire, and this uproar made by an intruder throws all of nature out of kilter.

First I start up the partridges in the stubble, then in the clover, then in a meadow, then along a hedge, then at the edge of a wood, then . . .

Suddenly I stop, in a sweat, and shout:

"Those insane birds! How they make me run!"

From a distance, I noticed something at the foot of a tree, in the middle of the meadow.

I come close to the hedge and look over.

It seems as though the neck and head of a bird are standing up in the shade of the tree. Immediately, my heart beats faster. There can be in that grass only partridges. When she heard me, the mother, by a signal they know, made them all lie flat. And she has flattened herself. Only her neck and head remain upright and watchful. But I hesitate, because the head does not move, and I am afraid of making a mistake, of firing on a root.

Here and there around the tree, yellow spots, either partridges or lumps of earth, further confuse me.

If I start them up, the branches of the tree will prevent me from aiming at them in flight, and I would prefer to fire at them on the ground, thereby committing what proper hunters call a murder.

But what looks like the neck of a partridge still does not move.

For a long time I lie low, watching.

If it really is a partridge, she is remarkable, with her immobility and her vigilance, and all those others, by the way they obey her, deserve this guardian. Not one moves.

I make a feint. I conceal myself entirely behind the hedge and stop, watching the partridge, because as long as I see her, she sees me.

Now we're all invisible, amid a deathly silence.

Then I take another look.

Ah! This time I'm sure! The partridge believed in my disappearance. The neck is still raised, and the movement she makes to bring it down gives her away.

Slowly I lift the butt of my rifle to my shoulder . . .

At night, tired and satisfied, before falling into a game-filled sleep, I think of the partridges I hunted during the day and imagine what their night may be like.

They are half-crazed.

Why are some of them missing?

Why are some in pain and, pecking at their wounds, unable to stay in place?

And why, suddenly, are they all full of fear?

They can hardly settle in a place now before the one on watch gives the alarm. They must be off again, leave the grass or the stubble.

They do nothing but flee, and are frightened even by the old familiar noises.

They no longer frisk around, or eat, or sleep.

They can't understand what is going on.

If a feather dropping from a wounded partridge were to tuck itself of its own accord into my proud huntsman's hat, I would see nothing out of the way in this.

As soon as it's too wet or too dry, or my dog is unable to follow a scent, or I aim badly and the partridges become unapproachable, I believe myself to be in a state of legitimate defense.

There are birds, the magpie, the jay, the blackbird, the thrush, with whom a self-respecting hunter does not enter into competition; and I respect myself.

I only enjoy taking on partridges.

They are so full of cunning!

In their cunning, they fly off in the distance; but you catch up with them and teach them a lesson.

They wait until the hunter has passed; but behind him they take flight too quickly, and he turns around.

They hide in deep clover; but he makes straight for it.

They turn in their flight; but that only brings them nearer.

They run instead of flying, and they run faster than a man; but there is the dog.

They call to each other when you separate them; but then they also call the hunter, and there is nothing more pleasing to him than their song.

The young couple had already begun living by themselves. I surprised them, one evening, at the edge of the plowed field. They flew off so close together, I might almost say with linked wings, that the shot that killed the one undid the other.

The one saw nothing and felt nothing, but the other had the time to see his companion dead and to feel himself dying beside her.

Together, on the same bit of earth, they left a little love, a little blood, and a few feathers.

Hunter, with one shot you made two fine hits: go tell your family about them.

The two old partridges from last year, whose brood was destroyed, loved each other no less than the young ones. I always saw them together. They were very clever at avoiding me, and I was not intent on pursuing them. I killed one of them by chance. And then I searched for the other one, to kill it too, out of compassion!

This one has a broken leg that hangs, as though I were restraining him by a thread.

That one follows the others until his wings give out; it falls, and runs; it runs as fast as it can ahead of the dog, lightly and half out of the furrow.

That other one has a piece of shot in his head. He separates himself from the rest. Dazed, he rises in the air, above the trees, higher than the cock on the steeple, toward the sun. And the hunter, filled with anxiety, has lost sight of him when at last he has to give in to the weight of his head. He closes its wings and drops like an arrow to plunge his beak into the ground.

And this one falls without a tremor, like a rag flung at a dog to train it.

Another, at the shot, wavers like a little boat and capsizes.

You can't tell why this one died, so secret is the wound under his feathers.

I quickly stuff this one into my pocket, as though I were afraid of being seen, of seeing myself.

But I must strangle the one that does not want to die. Between my fingers, he scratches the air, he opens his beak, his fine tongue flutters, and on his eyes, Homer says, the shadow of death descends.

Over there, the peasant lifts his head at my shot and looks my way.

That laboring man must be sitting in judgment on me; he will speak to me; in a solemn voice, he will put me to shame.

But not at all: either he's an envious peasant, miffed because he can't go hunting like me; or he's a good-natured, honest fellow, amused and eager to tell me where my partridges have gone.

He is never anyone indignantly speaking on behalf of nature.

This morning, after a five-hour walk, I turn toward home with my gamebag empty, my head hanging, my rifle heavy. The air is hot with an impending storm, and my dog, worn out, goes ahead of me, taking small steps, following the hedges, and, often, sitting down in the shade of a tree until I catch up.

Suddenly, as I am crossing some fresh clover, he drops, or rather flattens out, pointing: he points firmly, as motionless as a vegetable. Only the hairs at the end of his tail are trembling. I can take an oath there are partridges under his nose. They are there, all pressed together, sheltered from the wind and the sun. They see the dog, they see me, perhaps they recognize me, and, terrified, they don't move.

Shaken out of my torpor, I am ready and waiting.

My dog and I are not the first ones to move.

All of a sudden, and all together, the partridges rise, still pressed together as one, and my shot goes into them like a blow from a fist. One of them, stricken, whirls. The dog leaps on it and brings me a bloody rag, half a partridge. The fist did away with the rest.

There! We're not empty-handed! The dog frisks about, and I walk on with a swagger.

What I deserve is a load of lead in the hindquarters!

A Family of Trees

I come upon them after having crossed a plain burned by the sun.

They do not live by the side of the road, because of the noise. They inhabit waste fields, near a spring that only the birds know.

From a distance, they seem impenetrable. When I come nearer, their trunks separate. They receive me with caution. I am allowed to rest, to refresh myself, but I sense that they observe me with distrust.

They live together as a family, the oldest ones in the center, and the little ones, the ones whose first leaves have just been born, scattered around, but never very far.

They take a long time to die, and their dead are left standing until they crumble to dust.

They stroke each other with their long branches, to make sure they are all there, like blind people. They gesticulate in anger if the wind expends its breath trying to uproot them. But among themselves they never quarrel. They murmur together in perfect accord.

I feel that they must be my real family. I could soon forget the other one. Little by little, these trees will adopt me, and, in order to be deserving of this, I am learning what I must be able to do:

I already know how to look at passing clouds.

I also know how to stay in one place.

And I almost know how to be silent.

123

Le Cerf

The Stag

I entered the woods at one end of the path as he was coming in at the other.

At first, I thought that a stranger was approaching, carrying a plant on his head.

Then I discerned the little dwarf tree, with its spreading leafless branches.

At last, the stag appeared entire, and we both stopped.

I told him:

"Come closer. Don't be afraid. If I am carrying a rifle, it is only to give myself a countenance, and to look like a man who takes himself seriously. I never use it, and I leave the cartridges in their drawer."

The stag listened, sniffing my words. As soon as I stopped talking, he did not hesitate: his legs moved like stalks being crossed and uncrossed by the wind. He fled.

"What a pity!" I cried. "I was already imagining us walking along together. I would have fed you, by hand, your favorite herbs, and you, stepping at a leisurely pace, would have carried my rifle across your antlers."

L'Epervier

The Hawk

He begins by circling above the village.

He was just a fly, a speck of soot.

He grows larger as his circles tighten.

Now and then he remains immobile. The barnyard fowl show signs of worry. The pigeons get in under the roof. A hen calls back her chicks with a short cry, and the watchful geese can be heard cackling from one barnyard to the other.

The hawk hesitates, gliding about at the same height. Perhaps all he has in mind is to attack the cock on the church steeple.

He seems suspended in the sky by a thread.

All at once the thread breaks, the hawk drops, his victim chosen. Tragedy is about to strike in our midst.

But, to everyone's surprise, he stops before he reaches the ground, as though he lacked weight, and rises again with a stroke of his wing.

He has caught sight of me lying in wait for him at my door and holding behind my back something long and shining.